MAN

AND THE EARTH

by

Dr. Dan Q. Posin

designed and illustrated by

DAVID BURNSIDE

published by Lyons and Carnahan

staff editors:

Lester C. Babb

William R. Klueh

MEREDITH PRESS
Distributors to the trade for
Lyons and Carnahan

Library of Congress Catalog Card Number: 62-21459

CONTENTS

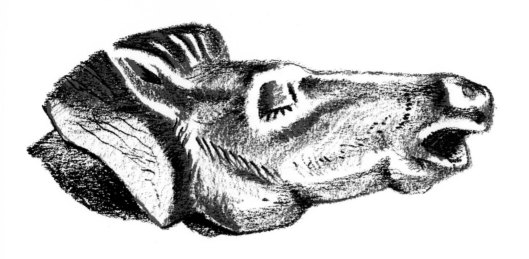

FOREWORD

Some 600 thousand years ago, perhaps even a million years ago, the marvelous laws and forces of nature brought into being the first primitive ancestors of Man. It is known that these man-like creatures roamed parts of the Earth; they looked and behaved like animals. At some moment, perhaps when trapped on a cliff by some hungry wolf, one of these man-like creatures perceived that a falling rock might be used as a defensive weapon. This was relating cause to effect, and if it happened that way, Man's long climb upward through the centuries could have begun about there.

Man, today, does not know precisely how it all began —but begin it did. After 600 thousand years, more or less, Man has become intelligent enough to blow his native Planet Earth to smithereens, and this may be just what will happen, too! It is strange to realize that Man has developed the skill and knowledge to create satellites to orbit the sun and planets, but has not developed the human compassion to live in peace with his neighbors. Wherever Man lives on Earth, he is a neighbor to other men. Political boundaries are so foolish in the face of Man's common heritage—humanity and hope.

On the cover of this book, our artist has painted the figure and features of a primitive Man curious about his native Earth. He holds warm soil in his hand, and he examines it intently. Perhaps our distant ancestor is wondering why material of the Earth is so soft and crumbly when dry, and so gummy and slippery when wet. Perhaps this primitive Man is wondering why trees and plants grow in soil; he may even be wondering if soil is good to eat. What is pictured most eloquently, we think, is the insatiable curiosity so characteristic of Man.

Earth is a planet spinning on its axis and revolving in its orbit in space. It is exactly the right distance from the sun to support the kind of life Man knows. If Earth were closer to the sun, the planet would be hotter, and Man would be different (if at all). And if Earth were farther from the sun, the planet would be colder, and Man would likewise be different (if at all).

But the great forces of nature have put Man onto this particular planet at this particular time and place in eternity. What has happened up to this time is merely prologue for what is yet to come. What seems important to Man, now, is that he examine his planet carefully. This he has done, first with his senses and later with his sciences. These findings are vividly told in MAN AND THE EARTH. The author, a distinguished scientist and scholar, dramatizes Man's awareness and appreciation of the human environment. There is a lot of science in this book, of course, but it is not a scientific book. With its beautiful, evocative art, MAN AND THE EARTH is simply an interesting and informative book written to stimulate the imagination and add to the knowledge of the reader.

—The Editors

Chapter I

THE PLANET EARTH

The Planet Earth is about 4.5 billion years old. Man has lived on it at least 600 thousand years and perhaps as long as a million years. Scientists keep finding new evidence of old life, which keeps them busy revising old estimates.

Man has always been curious about the origin of his planet, but the answer is hidden in the riddle of time and space. The origin of the universe is a vast mystery.

The solar system, of which Earth is a part, probably evolved from cosmic dust in endless space. Dust particles began to cling together. As their mass grew, so did their power of attraction. So, also, grew their heat. The greater the mass became, the faster did other particles move

toward it, and by friction increase the heat. The center of the mass grew blazing hot. In the course of eons, the inner fires of this great cloud of cosmic dust became the sun.

Material of the cosmic cloud which did not become a part of the sun began to coalesce and solidify in its turn. These separate actions finally took the form of nine planets orbiting the sun with their moons and other bodies. Within each planet, as within the sun, was a core of indescribable heat and fire. But while the sun is still too hot to permit any part of it to really cool, the fiery cores of the planets were eventually imprisoned in a cooling sheath or crust.

All of the planets in our solar system, as well as *all* bodies in space, exert an unrelenting pull upon other objects—a basic attraction. This is a force Man calls "gravity." The greater the mass and the smaller the radius, the greater the force of gravity.

However Man may speculate upon the origin of his particular solar system and his native planet, the fact remains that once upon an eon the Earth was a huge molten mass. Enormous pressures of internal gases and external weight forced the cooling crust to rise upward in mighty ridges and sink downward in gigantic chasms. An atmosphere was slowly created from escaping Earth vapors, and moisture began to condense in the sky. Rain

began to fall. Water began to accumulate in the Earth's low places. More moisture escaped from inside the Earth. Thus, greater amounts of water were drawn into the sky by the heat of the sun. This made more clouds, which made more rain fall, which made larger bodies of water accumulate on the Earth. In this gargantuan cycle there somehow occurred the miracle of chemistry that brought life into existence.

The familiar crust of the Earth is soil, rock, and water. Lying deep beneath the crust is solid rock. Below this are layers of iron and nickel. The core of the Earth is an incandescent mass of iron and nickel. Scientists report that this hot core of Earth may be nearly as hot now as it was in the very beginning—4.5 billion years ago.

Because of its rotation, the Earth has flattened out somewhat. The spinning tends to throw the planet's mid-section outward and flatten the polar sections slightly. If the Earth were sliced through along the polar axis, the cross section would not be a perfect circle, but a slight ellipse. One axis is longer than the other by about 28 miles. Actually, the Earth is very slightly pear-shaped —but without the stem.

Man-made satellites have taken many photographs of our planet from outer space. These show clearly the shape of the Earth, of its continents, and of its oceans. The pictures show cloud systems which enable us to foresee hurricanes and great cyclones in the upper atmosphere. The photographs very closely bear out the maps that were made by scientists before man-made satellites were

fact instead of fiction. It is explorations like these that
have caused Man to realize the Earth is not quite a perfect sphere floating in space, rotating, and revolving in
an orbit around the sun.

Our high-riding astronauts and the Soviet cosmonauts
have reported seeing strange particles in outer space.
Although some of the spacemen believe these objects to
be merely condensed exhaust from their spaceship, the
Russian astronomer, Vasily G. Fesenkov, has speculated
that the particles may be cosmic dust. There is some

speculation, too, that when astronauts fly far enough into the reaches of outer space, they will see that the Planet Earth has a tail like a comet.

Who knows what is possible, and what Man will learn? After all, in terms of relativity, the galaxies that fill unending space have been around for countless 'years,' while Man has been around for only a 'moment' or so.

Chapter II

WHAT THE EARTH IS MADE OF

Scientists know that the interior of the Earth is made up of hot metal and rock. Downward toward the incandescent center, temperature increases at a great rate. The diameter of the Earth is approximately 7,927 miles. Ambitious explorers penetrating the Earth's crust would have a long, hot hole to drill if they penetrated the Earth's core.

But the bottom of the ocean in some places is several miles closer to the center of the Earth than any place on any land surface. Hence there is a scientific plan under way to drill a few miles into the Earth from the bottom of the ocean. A few years ago this might have sounded fantastic, and it still might, but it can be done.

17

Scientists want to examine the Earth's mantle—that part of the Earth beneath the crust and above the molten interior. So far, much of what Man knows about the origin and composition of the Earth is scientific speculation based on certain proved facts. A look at the Earth's mantle could reveal the truth and do away with guesswork.

Is the Earth cooling, or warming? Does radioactivity make the inner furnace fires, or does the core of the Earth derive its heat from some other source? Is the composition of the planet *really* iron and nickel? Would there be fossils in the mantle so deep that scientists would know life existed billions of years earlier that Man now thinks? Would materials be found in the mantle to tell scientists how the Earth really originated?

Some drilling has already been done, with interesting results. Intricate and specially-designed ships are required for such operation. Off La Jolla, California, a recent drilling to a depth of 1,035 feet beneath the floor of the ocean took place in some 3,000 feet of water. This produced a gray-green core of clay which may be 25 million years old.

Of course, oil companies have been able to drill underwater wells as deep as 12 thousand feet, but this has been in shallow, protected waters.

Drilling in the open ocean will not be easy. The undertaking (in every sense of the word) will require from three to seven years to reach through about three miles of ocean and drill three miles of crust, and will cost maybe

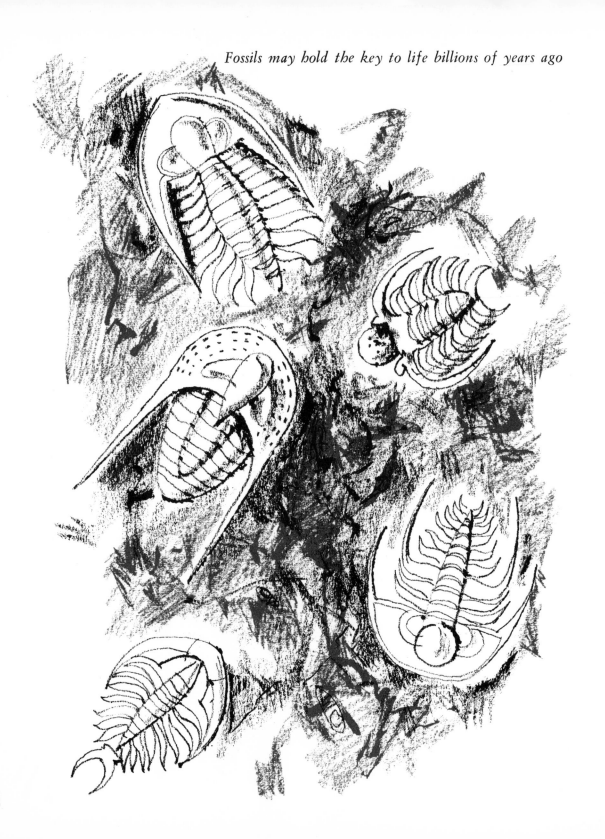

50 million dollars or more. Any scientific information is usually well worth its cost.

Scientific research is always valuable, not only in the form of pure knowledge, but in applications of that knowledge, too. The answers to many questions are still locked in the forbidding deeps of the oceans. But there are more questions—and each question answered raises more questions to be answered.

By studying the interior of the Earth, and soon by studying the structure of the moon, scientists may learn not only the origin of the Earth itself, but the origin of the entire solar system as well. There is reason to believe, for instance, that the mantle of the Earth and the surface of the moon are composed of the same type of rock.

Scientists can analyze the materials of the mantle—and the deep-lying crust also—to determine their mineral composition, density, conductivity of heat and electricity, and radioactivity. Each finding can tell a great deal more. The extent of the radioactivity—which produces heat—may tell us whether the Earth is cooling or warming up, and may make clear why there is such a surprisingly high flow of heat through the bottom of the ocean.

Scientists have advanced the theory that the rate of sedimentation deposit on the floor of the ocean amounts to about an inch every 2,500 years. The Earth has had some sort of oceans for a billion years or more, but the known sedimentation deposits suggest a time span of only 30 million years or so.

*The mantle of the Earth and the surface of the Moon
may be composed of the same type of rock*

Moreover, when scientists have dredged deep sea areas
without that first layer of sediment (such as those areas
surrounding submarine volcanoes) few rocks have been
found older than about 90 to 100 million years. Yet,
portions of continents which have at some epoch been
under shallow sea waters do have much sedimentary rock
substance.

This causes scientists to wonder about the possibility that the present ocean basins are not as old as they have been estimated to be. Or, perhaps the theoretical rate of ocean sedimentation is miscalculated. Or maybe some cataclysmic upheaval seriously changed the shape of the ocean bottoms and covered the ancient sedimentation with newer unsedimented matter. Perhaps some vast submarine seaquake shook the loose sedimentation of ages and rescattered it, more in some places than in others. It could be that quantities of the ancient sediment were washed ashore to become land somewhere. It could even be that the Earth's primordial seas and oceans were without suspended sediment for eons, although this does not seem likely.

The study of mantle cores may not only reveal the historical development of the planet, but fossils (if any are found) should provide a chronological catalog of the Earth's submarine events through the ages. Pre-prehistoric fossils of molds, algae, bacteria, and the like, would provide an important scientific insight into life on Earth in the long, long, long ago.

Perhaps a vast seaquake scattered the sedimentation of the ages

Another way Man may learn more about the inner structure of the Earth is through a concentrated and sustained study of earthquakes. Throughout all of the Earth's time, earth-moving tremors and shifts of great land masses have changed the face of the Earth. Man has always found one kind of explanation or another for the earthquakes which rocked the world around him.

Primitive Man blamed earthquakes on animals which dwelt beneath the land or the sea. In India, Man blamed the mole; in South America, the whale. In Japan, inventive Man blamed the catfish. Until now, nature has been the culprit causing earthquakes. But in the nuclear age, nations confront each other with blasting devices of such awesome magnitude that earthquakes seem to become trifles by comparison.

Most earthquakes are due to slippage along *faults* in the Earth. A fault is a crack in the Earth, caused by unequal cooling of adjoining layers of crust.

Great inner pressures may cause the two sides of a fault to slip against each other. When this happens, earthquake tremors occur. These are called tectonic earthquakes. Another type is a volcanic earthquake, caused by a powerful disturbance within a nearby volcano.

Earthquakes can be enormously destructive to the face and the structure of the land, as well as to the life upon it. One of the most famous earthquakes on record occurred in Lisbon, Portugal, in 1755. The tremors completely demolished the city, and killed thousands of people. The quake's shock waves rattled windows throughout Europe. Ocean tides swept up rivers, and lake waters raged for

Mole

Whale

Catfish

hours all over the continent. The earthquake occurred on All Saints' Day, so thousands of worshippers were crushed by the heavy stones of falling cathedrals.

Other historic quakes occurred in Shensai Province, China, in 1556, killing 830,000 people. An earthquake killed 300,000 in Calcutta, India, in 1737. More than 100,000 died in Tokyo's frightful quake and fire in 1923. In 1960, a huge quake shook loose an avalanche that swept down the mountain slopes and engulfed a Chilean village of 18,000. In mid-1962, an Iranian tremor killed tens of thousands, according to news reports of the day.

By contrast, San Francisco's famous earthquake of 1906 took the lives of only 452 people.

Shock waves produced during earthquakes are recorded by pressure-sensitive *seismographs* located at various stations on the Earth's surface. The seismograph is a remarkably sensitive instrument, recording even tiny tremors with a pen writing mechanically on a long roll of graph paper. The result is similar to the chart of a person's heartbeat when the doctor takes an electrocardiogram. In fact, maybe we can say that the Earth's heart is acting up during an earthquake—except that the disturbance originates not deep within Earth's bosom, but only slightly below the surface.

The seismograph measures the force of the shock waves at the site of the instrument. From this, and from a knowledge of how earthquake waves travel, it is possible to determine the point of origin and the original force (or scale) of the earthquake. Scientists exchange such

information freely, regardless of their own country's political orientation.

The material within the Earth has been found to be in constant movement. Most earthquakes occur in definite zones, known as earthquake belts. One example is the San Andreas earth fault running from north to south through California.

Earthquakes near the Earth's surface cause the most massive destruction to Man's establishments. However, scientists know that severe earthquakes occur as deep as 450 miles down in the Earth.

In order to better understand local geological formations, modern Man often creates his own earthquakes in a small way. Detonation of explosives placed in the Earth create shock waves. These waves are "read" by seismographs, and maps of the underground formations can be drawn from the recordings. The pattern of the waves indicates the structure of subsurface earth and rock in the area.

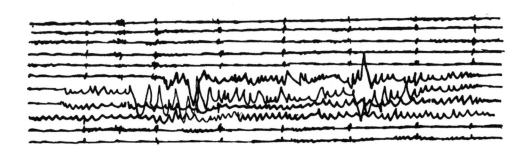

A seismograph records an earthquake

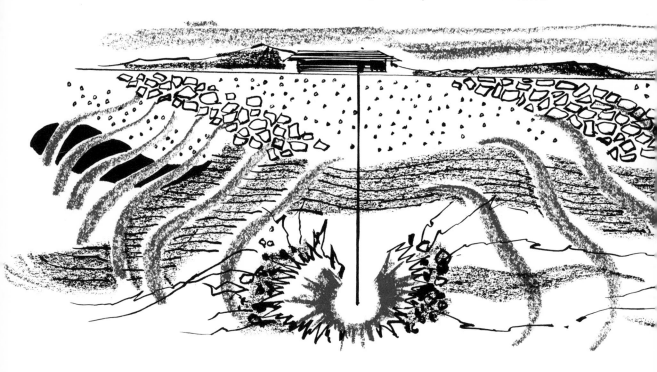

Locations of underground water, or of trapped organic matter such as gas, oil, or coal may be pin-pointed in this way. It can be said that the seismograph makes the Earth an open book, and a very large one, too.

For all practical purposes, the Planet Earth is a monster magnet. No one knows whether the Earth's magnetic properties came into being when the Earth was born, or whether a vast pliable mass spinning in the vacuum of outer space produces magnetic properties within itself. Magnetism is the subject of constant scientific study. Most of our rocket, missile, and satellite launchings include complex instruments to study some aspect of the Earth's magnetic field.

How can the Earth's magnetism be accounted for? Is it due to tremendous deposits of magnetic material deep within the planet? Could magnetism on this scale be caused by liquid electricity circulating in underground currents? Electricity does produce magnetism. Is the Planet Earth honeycombed inside by some fantastic network of liquid electricity?

But the idea of circulating electricity is probably correct. The Earth's high internal heat would surely destroy the magnetism of solid substances, say, of magnetic iron deposits.

Studies of the Earth's magnetism may lead to new insights about the construction of our very dense planet,

and the forces which are in it and around it. Sensitive scientific instruments are constantly being used to chart the Earth's internal and external magnetic fields.

Radioactivity within Earth has been mentioned. Some of the radioactive elements are uranium, thorium, radium, samarium, potassium; there are many others. These substances produce sub-microscopic nuclear explosions— particles and bursts of energy, and eventually heat. As an element emits particles, it turns into another element. Most radioactive elements eventually turn into *lead*.

Volcanoes are one of the Planet Earth's greatest mysteries. Many people think that a volcanic eruption and an earthquake occur together, and hence are the same thing. This is not necessarily so. A volcano can erupt violently without producing a great quake; a disastrous earthquake can occur without a volcano. But of course, a volcanic eruption and an earthquake can occur together.

One of history's most famous Earth disasters was the volcanic eruption and earthquake of Italy's brooding Mt. Vesuvius. In the year 79 A.D., the mountain shook violently and poured forth a mighty cascade of molten stone from deep within the Earth. Between the volcano and the Mediterranean Sea stood ancient Pompeii, a Roman city almost as lovely as Rome itself. The rivers of fire swept down the slopes and engulfed most of the city, and along with it, 16,000 citizens. When the Earth stopped shaking and the molten stone had cooled, a rain of volcanic ash fell steadily for days. Within a fortnight, Pompeii was buried, to remain hidden for centuries. This

long-ago disaster has been revealed little by little as
scholars and historians have excavated the ruins and reconstructed the story of that ancient, mighty earthquake.

Volcanoes are usually mountains. Sometimes volcanoes
have produced mountains, and sometimes mountains have
produced volcanoes. Mountains are great ridges of solid
matter thrust upward by titanic pressure within the Earth.
But a range of mountains can be honeycombed with weak
inner strata. In a sense, the crust of the Planet Earth is

like a ball filled with molten matter—wherever the container is weak, the material inside seeks to escape.

Oddly enough, the Earth's crust may be weakest in the upthrust masses of mountains. The molten inner mass of the Earth, under the vast pressures of a constantly cooling and shrinking crust, flows upward into the mountains' cracks, crevices, faults, and other flaws. Eventually the molten matter melts its way to the surface and pours forth in a fiery river. This is a volcanic eruption.

Sometimes the molten matter deep within the Earth finds a weak place in the plains or prairies of the Earth's crust. Then a curious eruption takes place. A volcano is born, and forms its own mountain. Such a strange phenomenon is the volcano called Paricutin, near Michoacan in west central Mexico.

On February 20, 1943, a native farmer found in his cornfield a small area of boiling, burning soil. Even as he watched, chunks of cinder-like matter, rather like hot asphalt, began pushing up. Literally, the cinders bubbled forth in an ever-increasing cone. In the weeks that followed, scientists came from all over the world to study this unique display of bizarre forces. The eruption has continued unabated ever since. The cone has grown until it now towers nearly 2,500 feet above the plain on which it stands. The eruption still goes on, hour after hour, with no end in sight.

Volcanoes can erupt under water quite as readily as in the mountains or in an open field. On October 1, 1957, a sub-marine eruption took place in the ocean near the

Portuguese Azores. The sea boiled and raged with gases, steam, and violent agitation. Out of the depths there finally rose an island, almost a mile square. When the erupted material had, within 30 days, reared upward to the height of a 30-story building, the whole island disappeared in a mighty explosion. A few days later a volcano's cone began emerging from the sea. Molten lava poured outward and downward into the steaming ocean, and another island was formed. The eruption stopped a a year later, but from deep within the Earth enough matter had poured forth to make a new island more than a mile square; its volcanic cone now rises 530 feet above the surface of the ocean.

One of the most violent volcanic explosions in recorded history took place in 1883. The entire island of Krakatoa, located in the Sunda Strait between Java and Sumatra, disappeared during three days of cataclysmic blasts. Before Krakatoa was obliterated by the blasts, its volcanic cone stood nearly 3,000 feet above the waters of the Indian Ocean and the Java Sea.

At first the eruptions were mild, but they became increasingly violent. Finally, a mighty blast cracked the entire island wide open. The ocean waters rushed in to meet the white-hot lava, and the gigantic explosions left no trace of the beautiful island except a great cavern more than 1,000 feet below sea-level.

This mighty blast, not unlike a thermo-nuclear explosion, sent a towering black cloud of volcanic dust and debris about 20 miles into the atmosphere. The winds

A volcanic island emerges near the Azores

carried the volcanic ashes in all directions until the skies were darkened for a distance of 150 to 200 miles.

The sun's rays reflecting on the dust particles high above the Earth made multi-hued sunsets which were seen for days all around the world.

Mighty tidal waves surged over the nearby islands, destroying ships and villages. Between 30 and 40 thousand people were killed by the rampaging waters. The gigantic waves continued unabated until they reached the large continents of Antarctica, Africa, India, and Indonesia.

Sometimes a violent volcanic explosion will blow the entire top off of a lofty mountain. When this happens, much of the molten lava from deep inside the volcano will be hurled far up into the atmosphere. The great molten masses cool and fall gack to Earth as huge chunks of lava rock. Their weird, fantastic shapes often come to rest many miles from the core of the volcano from which they came. When the volcano becomes extinct, water fills the deep depression and forms a beautiful lake.

Crater Lake in southwestern Oregon was formed by just such volcanic action. It is the deepest lake in North America. Its waters are more than 2,000 feet deep and lie 2,000 feet below the rim of the volcanic cone of once mighty Mount Mazama. This giant of the Cascade Range erupted about 6,500 years ago. The Indians call Mount Mazama the mountain that "swallowed its head."

Geologists are not altogether sure what causes volcanic eruptions, but undoubtedly heat is the basic cause. Some of the heat may be left over from the formation of the

Earth, but most of it is probably caused by the break-
down of unstable elements such as uranium, thorium, and
potassium. You remember that these elements are radioactive and emit particles and *heat,* and then eventually
change into lead. But the most common lavas are not
made up of rocks which contain these radioactive elements. Radioactivity itself is not entirely the cause of
volcanoes.

Scientists have counted about 430 volcanoes which are
now active or which recently were active. There are many
times this number of extinct volcanoes. More than 80

Grapes growing on the fertile slopes of Vesuvius

per cent of the Earth's volcanic activity occurs in the Pacific Ocean or in bordering land masses. A great number of volcanoes are also found in what is known as the Mid-Atlantic Ridge, which stretches under water all the way from Iceland to Tristan da Cunha in the South Atlantic—a third of the distance around the world.

Volcanoes are also known along the borders and forelands of the Alpine-Himalayan belt, and in the Indian Ocean.

Although volcanoes are tremendously destructive, they can help to nourish and sustain life. Volcanic ash, as it decomposes through the years, forms enormously rich soils. Many of Man's most important food crops depend in part on volcanic soils.

43

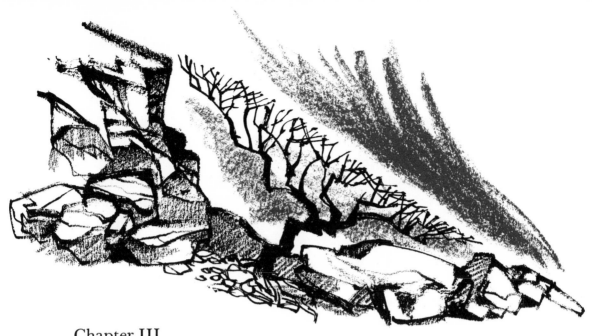

Chapter III

TIME, THE EARTH'S GREAT LEVELER

Not only have volcanoes and earthquakes changed the landscape of Man's native Earth, but so have unending centuries of sun, wind, water, and weather. In daylight, the sun's heat expands the Earth's matter exposed to it; when hot sunlight yields to the cool night, the Earth's matter contracts. This slight, simple process, continued for thousands upon thousands of years, will eventually reduce a mountain of granite to a heap of broken rubble.

Through the years of the past, wind has used particles of Earth and grains of sand as tiny chisels. As a strong wind sweeps close to the Earth, it picks up trillions of these particles and hurls them at any obstacle before it. Soft rock, soil, and debris wear away quickly; the harder material takes more time. This wear-away is called erosion; it accounts for many of the fantastic rock forms to be found in the American West and elsewhere over the face of the Earth.

But while the Earth is thus eroded away in one place, it is built up in another. Whatever Earth debris is picked up and blown about by the wind is eventually dropped to Earth somewhere else. This wind erosion is really a matter of rearranging the Earth's landscape.

Much the same action occurs when water is the eroding agent. Soil and sand suspended in rushing water can erode the stream beds as readily as wind-borne particles. The world's most impressive example of erosion is America's Grand Canyon. The Colorado River, rising high in the Rocky Mountains, once flowed toward the continent's west coast across a relatively level plain that is now Arizona. This colossal erosion began millions of years ago, and is continuing even today. In those thousands of centuries, the Colorado River has carved a canyon a mile or more deep, four to 18 miles wide, and 217 miles long.

The walls of the canyon are eroded by water, wind, and weather into a weird landscape of strange and massive mesa and tower forms. The layers upon layers of soil and stone exposed by the erosion reveal clearly the story of that part of the Earth when it lay under primordial seas. Fossils and matter found in the strata tell us of the area's submergence, the deposition of primitive marine matter, and the gradual uplift which drained away the sea and created a flat plain on that part of the continent.

The Grand Canyon

Another splendid example of water and wind erosion lies in the western slopes of the Colorado Rockies. There, another smaller river rising high and coursing westward, has cut a spectacular chasm in the Earth's crust. Unlike the Grand Canyon, the Black Canyon of the Gunnison is very narrow, about a quarter of a mile wide on the average, yet it is 1,500 feet deep in solid gneiss rock, granite, and quartz. It takes its name from early explorers, who found that sunshine rarely penetrated the canyon's greatest depths.

49

In the oceans, coral reefs or atolls are an example of slow, steady building over many years. Atolls occur near land masses that are near the equator. These atolls are narrow ridges of "rock" near the surface of the ocean, and are formed from the skeletons of little marine animals. The two main species are corals and mullipores. As these little sea-animals die, their skeletons pile one on top of the other, building up the reef. The reef is also built up by waves and storms which tear off blocks of rock and pile them on top of the reef. Sometimes little islands are formed. These islands will often be covered with plants and other forms of life.

Among the mighty forces that have moulded the Earth's crust are the great glaciers. These towering mountains of ice have crept out of the Arctic three times during the last 600,000 years, covering most of the Northern Hemisphere.

The enormous weight and pressures of the glaciers scraped deep gullies in the crust of the Earth, leveled hills, and tore great rocks from mountains. The glaciers carried masses of soil, rocks, and debris across the land for hundreds of miles, leaving strange, alien deposits all over the Northern Hemisphere.

The Black Canyon of the Gunnison

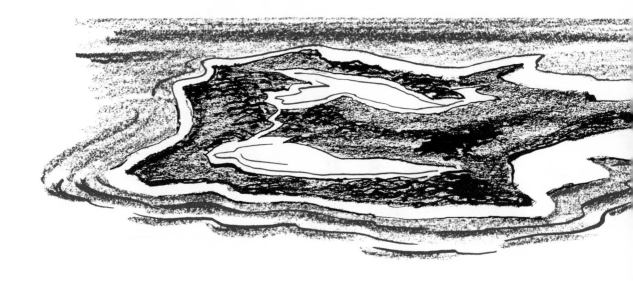

After each advance, a warm period intervened; the ice sheets melted, and life flourished once more in the temperate zones. We are now living in the Fourth Interglacial Period. Scientists are not sure if the great glaciers are gone forever. They might come again in another 100,000 years or so.

The true outer layer of the Planet Earth is not its crust, but its atmosphere, the sea of gas and dust in which we live. The atmosphere is only a small part of the Earth—about a millionth by weight—but it is *our* part, more than any other. We actually live at the bottom of an ocean of gas.

The Earth's atmosphere is many miles deep. By far the greater part of the atmosphere is concentrated within the first few miles nearest the crust of the Earth. This part, the *troposphere,* extends upward about seven miles

Coral

from sea level. Only the first three miles or so will maintain life. Above this point, the air thins out so greatly that life generally has a hard time maintaining its hold.

Above the life-sustaining troposphere are a number of atmospheric layers which play important roles in Man's affairs. In the stratosphere the bands of ozone, for example, filter harmful ultraviolet rays coming from the sun. Layers of ionized gas and dust within the ionosphere serve as natural reflectors for Man's radio waves. Still further up are huge bands of radiation, called the Van Allen Zones.

The part of Earth's atmosphere in which we take the most direct interest is the troposphere, that part in which we live. This turbulent layer is responsible for the rains, winds, hailstorms, lightning, and fogs, which affect all people.

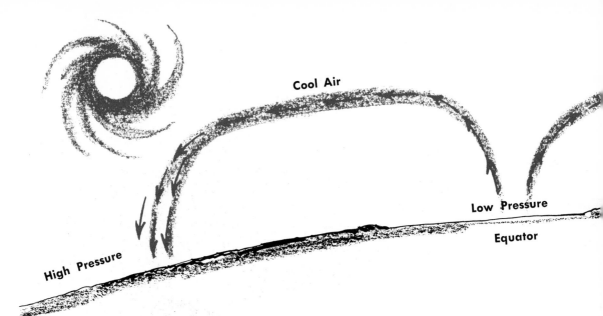

Cool Air

Low Pressure

Equator

High Pressure

The most important object in the weather picture is the sun, which heats the air and thus creates movement. The hot air rises, and we have the beginning of a never-ending sequence of events. The sun, it might be said, "drives" the atmosphere. The sun is the basic source of all natural power known to Man.

It could be said that the sun and the atmosphere combine to form a sort of heat engine. Or, the sun and the atmosphere are a sort of air conditioner for Man and his Planet Earth.

Air becomes hot at the equator, so it becomes light and therefore rises. When it reaches the cooler regions of the higher altitudes, the air cools and rises no more, but flattens out. Soon the air is so heavy it sinks downward again. Where it descends—at the downward point of the first loop—the air piles up. At this place, the air pressure is very strong. Where the process started—at the equator—there is a lack of air, so the air pressure is relatively weak.

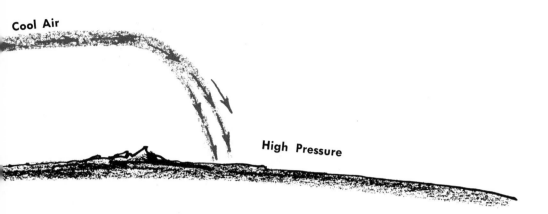

Cool Air

High Pressure

In a similar way, there are other loops and pressure regions. Where the air pressure is light, there is a partial vacuum. Air from the higher pressure regions flows toward the lower pressure regions. Because of the Earth's rotation, the air does not flow *straight* up or down—or directly north or south. The Earth's rotation deflects the air. Such a deflection occurs even when a shell is fired from a gun.

The mountains, oceans, and other natural surface structures of the Earth also play a part in determining the weather that an area may get. Mountains force air to rise, cool, and lose its moisture by raining. This means that the places then visited by the air get dry weather. Lakes and oceans make the air above them moist and damp. Deserts heat the dry air, causing it to rise.

The seasons on Planet Earth are due to the Earth's tilted position relative to the sun as the Earth revolves it. When the sun is overhead, north of the Earth's equator, it is winter in the Southern Hemisphere; conversely, when the sun is overhead, south of the Earth's equator, it is winter in the Northern Hemisphere.

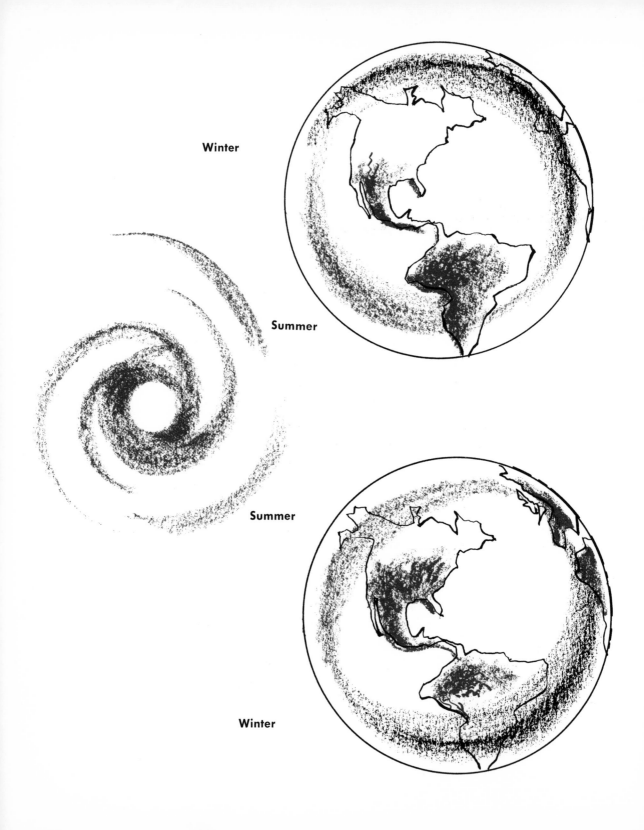

Winter

Summer

Summer

Winter

The Earth's axis of rotation remains almost parallel to itself, through winter and summer, year after year. Actually, this axis slowly leans and rotates, but in one year it hardly shows; after thousands of years, it does show.

This tilting motion of the axis is called "precession." It is due to the moon and sun pulling on the equatorial bulge of the Earth, first above the equator, and then below it. As the moon and sun pull the bulge, the whole axis tilts and also rotates. It is as if the Earth were a slowly rotating top, made to wobble by the force of gravity. The moon, though much less massive than the sun, is much closer to Earth. Thus, the moon's pull is greater than the pull of the sun in this cosmic tug of war.

The Earth also experiences regular flows of large bodies of water—the tides—which are due to the gravitational pull of the moon and the sun.

The moon pulls upon the nearer waters, and they come forward; it also pulls upon the Earth, but with less force, because the Earth's center is further away from the moon than are the nearer waters. Finally, the moon also pulls on the far waters, but not as much as upon the Earth! The net result is that the near waters are pulled away from the Earth, while the Earth is pulled away from the far waters. As the Earth rotates, every place along any seashore should get high tide and low tide twice every 24 hours.

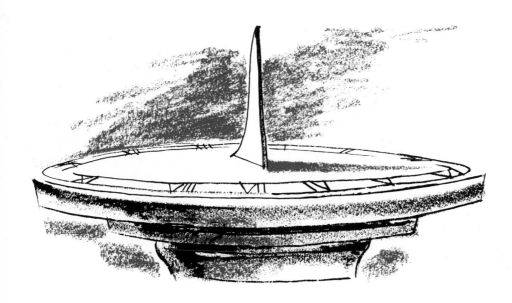

Chapter IV

THE GEOLOGIC ERAS

Time has no beginning perceptible to Man. Since Man has been able to think, he has used an arbitrary time measurement. In the distant past, it can be speculated that time was crudely measured by the days and seasons of primitive Man. Nowadays, Man uses calendars and clocks.

But scientists think in terms of eons, eras, ages, epochs.

In the mid-1930's, H. W. Van Loon, the historian, told a fanciful story about a mighty mountain of solid iron at some mystic place in the far north. Once every thousand years, he wrote, a small bird flies to this mountain to sharpen its beak. When the tiny creature has done this

Van Loon's "mighty mountain of solid iron"

often enough to wear the great mountain of iron down to a flat plain, then will have passed one "day" in eternity.

Without some frame of reference in time, it is impossible to discuss the history of the Earth and the development of Man. So, scientists have established a table of Geologic Eras.

Uranium atoms give off a particle and each atom then changes into another substance: thorium. The thorium atom gives off a particle, and changes into still another substance. This substance also gives off a particle and changes. The change process continues through about 15 substances, at the end becoming lead. So if scientists went to some far-distant planet and found rocks which contained a lot of lead and not much uranium, they would know that the rocks and the planet were both very old.

On the contrary, if the rocks were found to contain considerable uranium and very little lead, the rocks and the planet would of course be much younger.

Using this method, plus what is known about the formation of the sun, plus investigations of meteors that fall upon Earth from outer space, scientists compute that the Earth is indeed about 4.5 billion years old. Ages of various deposit areas, from the surface of the Earth downward, can be determined by purely geological means.

Although Man may have lived on the Earth for more than a million years, there is still much to be learned about the Earth. During 1958 and 1959, scientists from all parts of the world combined their efforts in a systematic study of the Earth and the sun. Their findings are at this time still being interpreted.

A Tabulation of Geologic Eras

Years ago	Name of Age	Earliest Animal Life
2,300,000,000	Archeozoic	
1,420,000,000	Proterozoic	protozoa, one-celled animals
620,000,000	Paleozoic	reptiles fishes amphibians insects
100,000,000	Mesozoic	mammals birds
70,000,000	Cenozoic	placental mammals
700,000		mankind

Another atomic method of determining the passage of time is the carbon-14 dating technique.

All living organisms, plant or animal, contain the element carbon. Most of the carbon is known as carbon-12, but a certain percentage is known as carbon-14. Carbon-14 is radioactive, and keeps breaking down into something else. But because carbon-14 is constantly being produced

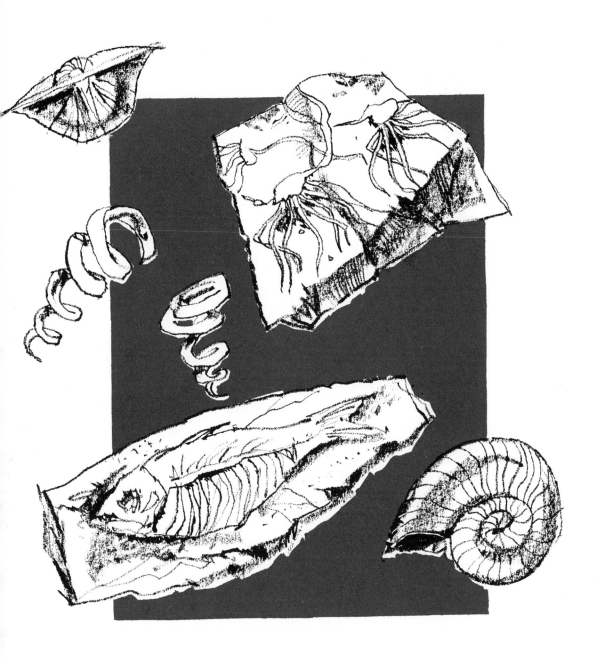

The carbon-14 method can determine the age of fossils

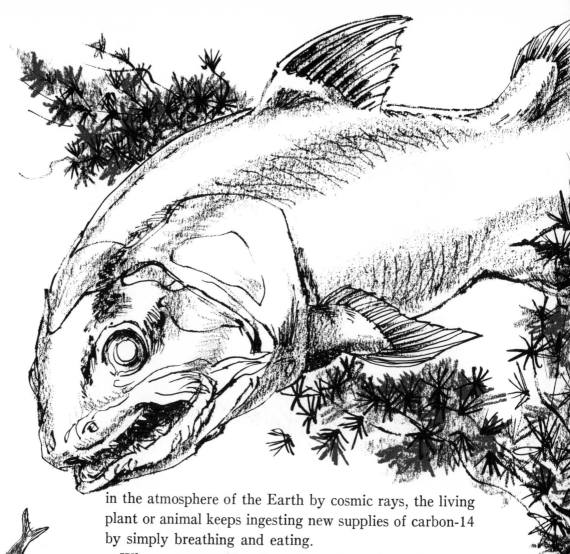

in the atmosphere of the Earth by cosmic rays, the living plant or animal keeps ingesting new supplies of carbon-14 by simply breathing and eating.

When an organism dies, its carbon-14 continues to change into something else, but the dead plant or animal can no longer take in new supplies of carbon-14. So the carbon-14 the plant or animal had at the time of death will disintegrate at a fixed rate without replenishment.

Scientists have found that carbon-14 has a half-life of 5,600 years. That is, after 5,600 years there is only half as much carbon-14 left as there was when death occurred. Each 5,600 years thereafter, the amount of carbon-14 is decreased by 50 per cent. Naturally, the longer the organism has been dead, the less carbon-14 can be found in the fossil remains. The rate of carbon-14 disintegration is a constant that never changes.

Geologists find carbon-14 dating a very useful method for determining the age of most of the bones and fossils they find. But there is one great limitation: after 30 thousand years, almost all carbon-14 is gone from any organic substance. If an organic fossil is found with no carbon-14 in it at all, the life form could have been dead for 60 thousand years, 600 thousand years, or six million years or even more.

The carbon-14 method cannot be used to determine the age of the Earth itself—only some of the Earth's fossils.

But scientists keep trying, and science is a most flexible tool for learning. A new method of time-determination has been developed. Potassium-40 produces argon-40 at a known rate. The half life of potassium-40 is much longer than the half life of carbon-14. Time can be determined as far back as 50 million years by measuring the amount of argon-40 in an organic fossil.

Much of what Man has learned about his prehistoric past has been learned from studying fossils of men who lived hundreds of thousands of years ago.

Fossil remains of early Man are much harder to find than the fossil remains of animals that lived long ago. The bones of the early men who lived in prehistoric times seldom became fossilized. Prehistoric men probably were not buried, and their bones were destroyed by the elements, or were eaten by animals.

However, in some of the old limestone caves where prehistoric Man lived, the bones were sealed in by cave deposits and preserved. When a scientist who is a specialist in anatomy studies these fossilized bones, he can learn much about the body structure of these men who lived long, long ago.

Anthropologist Louis Leakey and his wife, a team of extraordinary scientists interested in the development of Man, discovered some bone fossils in Tanganyika, East Africa. These fossils resemble human skeletons. By the argon-40 method, the Leakeys have computed their fossils to be at least 1,750,000 years old. Since the fossil bones are similar to human bones, scientists are beginning now to wonder if man-like life has not existed on Earth far earlier than has heretofore been thought. But much remains to be verified before this information becomes an accepted part of Man's scientific knowledge.

A giant Sequoia redwood

As the Earth grew old, the land lowered and lifted, the seas moved onto or drained from part of the continents, and this teeter-totter process formed sedimentary rocks. As the sediment formed, it sometimes covered plants and animals before decay set in. The entombing sediment became rock; it protected the hard parts of the plants or animals—bones, teeth, shells, or leaves—and kept them from decomposing entirely. Each sediment layer left by the seas was pressed by more and more sediment, and formed into hard rocks. The plant and animal parts were pressed, too. Now, millions of years later, where the sedimentary rock has worn away, scientists find some of these original teeth or bones. Sometimes the original teeth and bones have been replaced by minerals, but their shape still remains.

Man today is aware of several "living fossils" upon his Planet Earth; the great sequoia redwoods of California were saplings a thousand years before the beginning of the Christian Era; native fishermen on the Island of Malagasy (Madagascar) have several times caught and preserved for scientific study a deep-sea coelecanth —a strange, curious fish with primitive hands and feet. Until recently, the coelecanth was thought to have become extinct many thousands of years ago. Almost every American knows the harmless opossum, which, by all scientific criteria ought to have become extinct centuries upon centuries ago. So not all "fossils" are dead ones. Many are alive, and walk among us like ghosts out of the past. How exciting life is, how eternally amazing.

An opossum with young

Chapter V

MAN UPON THE EARTH

Man emerged upright from the shadows of time, perhaps as much as 600 thousand years ago. Certainly, within Man's present knowledge, not longer than 1,750,000 years ago. Scientists say that Man is one of a *group of vertebrate creatures,* or, Man is a creature with an internal skeleton and a vertebrate spine.

Man also is of the mammal class, which means that his young are born alive and they are nourished from the breast of the mother. Because he uses his fingers and brains, Man is a *primate;* because he walks erect on two legs, he is of the *Hominidae Family.* Man is of the *Genus homo,* and because he thinks, he is finally cataloged as the species of *Homo-sapiens*—"Man the wise."

So we have:

Group:	Vertebrate
Class:	Mammal
Order:	Primate
Family:	Hominidae
Genus:	Homo
Species:	Homo-sapiens

It is sobering to think that Man developed for at least 60 thousand centuries only to become a six-name Latin category in the classification charts of animals. But ironic as it may be, these few words are the scientific description of Man, and it applies to *all* men, wherever they may be on the planet, and of whatever race or color. Men may not yet be able to accommodate themselves to the idea of a common kinship for all mankind, but science does.

In the beginning, Man was beset on every side by a nature that demanded adaptation of those creatures that wished to survive. Man lived in a wild and hostile world. The weak, the stupid, the slow, and the unfortunate failed to adapt quickly and were lost. The "fittest" survived; on the long trail upward, the first law of nature became the survival of the fittest.

When Man was very primitive, 600 thousand years ago, he fought wild animals, adverse weather, violent storms, floods, earthquakes, fires, famines, and drouths, and all the other phenomena of nature that can make life miserable on the face of the Earth, including other men.

Six hundred thousand years ago Man fought wild animals

But because he walked erect, because he could use his hands and feet, and because he could *reason* and *think* (although not very well at first, and not too nobly even today) Man began slowly to adapt to his environment no matter how it changed.

Man fought to survive the onslaughts of nature, and still he knew further need to fight—he bore within him the instinct of combat. He fought animals, and used their meat and hides to provide food, clothing, and shelter. After Man was able to fight and defeat animals, he began to fight other men. This is a primitive instinct in men that perhaps will someday die.

But even as Man fought other men, he also learned to live and work with other men. He established villages, developed a sort of social system, cleared trees from the

Animal meat and skins provided food, clothing and shelter

Earth—Man began to use the Earth. He discovered that in the soil grew good things to eat. He used soil to build barricades; he used soil for shelters; he used soil for pots and vessels; he used soil to color himself with ceremonial patterns and symbols. Man used the soil to cover his dead. The Earth became more and more important to Man; the Earth became a god, a protector, a mother.

And when Man rested he looked upon the sky—the moon, the sun, the stars—and upon the Earth he drew their images as he saw them; when he could, Man carved these likenesses in stone and wood. From the native materials of the Earth he built symbols for his tribe and his gods, and these were totems. When all this had come to pass, Man had found the terms upon which he could live in his wild and hostile world. He had learned to

survive the fury of nature, the savagery of fierce and hungry animals, the fear and hatred of other men.

As he exhausted his nearby food supply, Man began to roam from place to place, hunting food elsewhere. Man moved over the face of the Earth. If centuries could be compressed one upon another like a slow motion moving picture, there would be revealed swirls and eddies of men drifting restlessly about on most of the world's continents.

Through necessity—through the need to find new supplies of food—and through natural, inborn curiosity, Man wandered over the Planet Earth — exploring, fighting, adapting, and surviving.

Man learned, as he drifted upward through the centuries, that the skins of animals would keep him warm when the winds of winter were wild and bitter. Man discovered, finally, that with the skins of animals he could also make his own shelter wherever he wished.

Man learned that overlapping large green leaves would keep him dry in violent rainstorms. He found that dried clay in his campsite fireholes would hold water indefinitely. He found that by using green sticks or flat rocks he could carry fire from place to place. He found that where any green thing grew in the hot, dry places, water was not far underground. Shade from the blazing sun could be made with rocks piled together to form walls, and the walls could protect him from animals and other

men. Man found, through the centuries, that if he could not adapt his environment to himself, he at least could adapt himself to his environment.

In the Earth's frigid climates, Man found snow itself could be used to make a warm and cozy shelter. The skins of wild beasts could be used to keep Man as warm as the living animals had been. Creatures of the sea and the great, snowy wastes—the seal, the walrus, the whale, the waterbirds, the arctic hares, the polar bears, wolves, caribou, and musk ox—all the living things that had in preceding eons themselves adapted to the frigid climate —provided the means for Man to adapt himself to the same icy conditions.

In the Earth's tropical jungles, Man responded to the same sort of stimulus—he learned to survive in the thick, steaming heat by wearing no clothes at all. His skin became dark, like the surrounding jungle. Food was

Man made stone walls for shade and protection

everywhere for the taking, and shelter was easy to find.
He had only to climb the great gnarled limbs of the
nearest banyan tree.

When Man's environment changed, he changed with it
or adapted to it. When the long cold of the Ice Age
brought frigid weather to the once temperate zones of
the Northern Hemisphere, Man retreated before the ad-
vancing ice sheets. During the warm Interglacial Period,
he wandered back to the areas from which his ancestors
had fled.

In 1952 an excavation in southern Illinois laid bare an ancient campsite of early American Man. The excavation revealed charcoal and fossil bones of small animals which the campers had eaten. The carbon-14 dating method showed the charcoal to be more than 11,000 years old. At that time the great glacier was less than 400 miles away and still covered Wisconsin and Minnesota.

In those places of the Earth where seasons came and went, Man followed the animals as they migrated. They were his food supply on the move. On the plains, the low mountains, and in the vast, dry deserts, Man became a nomad who lived lightly and traveled far.

At all times and everywhere, as Man migrated into more and more places through the passing centuries, he became both the product and the master of his environment. Man was a child of the Earth; the Earth was parent to this upright mammal that had learned to reason and think, to adapt, and to survive in a wild and hostile world.

Chapter VI

THE AGES OF WEATHER

Man had no sooner learned to live with nature than some phenomenal change in the temperature of the Earth's atmosphere brought forth the long cold. Water all over the planet's northern hemisphere turned bitter cold. Snowstorms, sleetstorms, hailstorms, built up to a freezing fury. Layer after layer, the frozen water accumulated into gargantuan sheets of solid ice. Enormous weight created irresistible pressures, and the ice sheets began creeping out of the north like vast towering walls of frosted glass.

Living creatures of all kinds fled ahead of the monstrous glaciers, but many animals sank in bogs or swamps, to be entombed forever or until discovered by curious Man in succeeding epochs. Others were trapped by the bliz-

A sabre-toothed cat is trapped in a bog

zards in the hills and mountains, on the plains, and in the great forests. Man came to realize more fully the relationship between cause and effect; he wandered before the ice sheets in great migratory waves, moving wherever food and warmer weather were to be found.

Planet Earth has known four main ages of Ice. The first of the great glaciers began to move south over Europe about one million years ago, and south over North America some 600 thousand years ago. The entire northern hemisphere of the Planet Earth was eventually covered with ice and snow. All living creatures of the Earth were driven into the lands girdling the equator, or south of it.

The environment of Man changed radically, but Man changed with it.

Then, in a manner of speaking, the glaciers retreated. Man and animals returned from the equatorial regions and began life again in the temperate climates. This is called the First Interglacial Period, and it began a little more than half a million years ago. Three more times the Ice Ages returned, about every hundred thousand years or so; after about an equal time, the cold would retreat to permit an Interglacial Period. Thus there have been four Ice Ages upon the Earth, always marching forth upon the land from the frigid north.

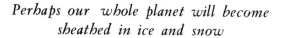

*Perhaps our whole planet will become
sheathed in ice and snow*

It might be said that we are now living in the Fourth Interglacial Period. Scientists today are not sure the great glaciers are gone forever. Perhaps the cold will come again after another hundred thousand years have passed. Perhaps the ocean waters will freeze into massive glaciers and cause the oceans to become much shallower; perhaps in some far distant future there will once more be land bridges between all the continents, or perhaps the whole planet will become sheathed in ice and snow, and Man will become extinct upon the Earth. Some people speculate that Man has come to depend so much on machines and science that he has lost his native ability to adapt and survive, as did his primordial ancestors.

And how many ancestors have there been? How many people have been born since the beginning of the human race? What percentage does the present world population of three billion represent of the total number of people who have ever lived?

The Population Reference Bureau, Inc., of Washington, D. C., recently published a study which offers a scholarly calculation of the answers based on known facts.

This estimate assumes that Man first appeared about 600 thousand years ago, a date which has been proposed for the dawn of Man's prehistoric era. Since then, the bureau estimates that about 77 billion babies have been born. Thus, today's population of approximately three billion is about four per cent of that number.

The study states that absolutely no information exists as to the size and distribution of prehistoric populations. Presumably they were not large, nor very widely distributed. If the 600 thousand B.C. date is accepted as a sound compromise between several schools of thought on the subject, then only about 12 billion people—less than one sixth of the total number ever born—are estimated to have lived before 6,000 B.C.

Anthropologists and scientists differ by hundreds of thousands of years as to when Man first walked upon this Earth. Recent discoveries, as has been indicated, suggest that the life span of the human species might date back as much as 1,750,000 years.

If the "beginning" actually extended a million years prior to 600,000 B.C., the report estimates the number of births prior to 6,000 B.C. would be 32 billion, and the total number an estimated 96 billion.

Chapter VII
THE AGES OF MAN

Man does not easily comprehend the enormous amount of time that has elapsed since his earliest Man-like ancestors first started the long climb toward civilization. Years, months, weeks, days — even centuries — are such small gradations of time in comparison to the total time elapsed that they are inadequate for measuring so many hundreds of thousands of years.

Since Man in one way or another categorizes and tabulates everything he knows, it follows naturally that he has a tabulation of his own physical development since he stepped forth from the mists of time as a thinking creature. The following tables are not intended to be a rigorous scientific tabulation, but rather a handy frame of reference.

The Ages of Man

70,000,000 B.C.	First Primate (Europe)
30,000,000 B.C.	Anthropoid Apes (Europe)
700,000 B.C.	Ice Ages begin
600,000 B.C.	Zinjanthropus Man (Africa)
500,000 B.C.	Java Man (Asia)
400,000 B.C.	Chellean Man (Africa)
360,000 B.C.	Peking Man (Asia)
250,000 B.C.	Steinheim Man (Europe)
150,000 B.C.	Fontechevade Man (Europe)
100,000 B.C.	Neanderthal Man (Europe)
35,000 B.C.	Combe Capelle Man (Europe)
28,000 B.C.	Cro-Magnon Man (Europe)
23,000 B.C.	Rhodesian Man (Africa)
20,000 B.C.	American Indian
14,000 B.C.	Magdalenian Man (Europe)
8,000 B.C.	Modern Man

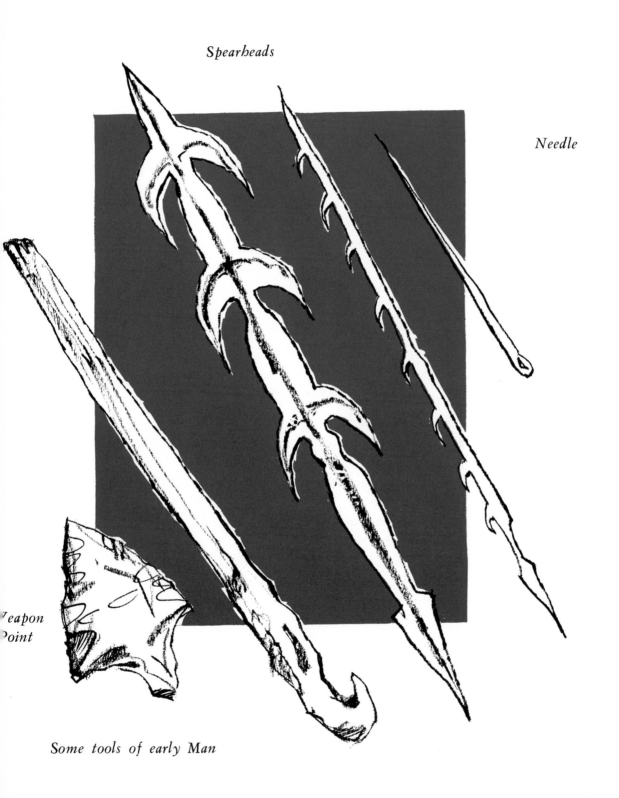

Spearheads

Needle

Weapon
Point

Some tools of early Man

Man has a cultural as well as a physical development. A simplified table would chart Man's progress as modern scientists have reconstructed the climb upward from prehistory.

The Cultures of Man

Stage	Years Ago B.C.		
Abbevillian	500,000	to	300,000
Acheulian	300,000	to	100,000
Mousterian	100,000	to	35,000
Lower Perigordian	35,000	to	28,000
Aurignacian	28,000	to	21,000
Upper Perigordian	21,000	to	18,000
Solutrean	18,000	to	14,000
Magdalenian	14,000	to	8,000
Mesolithic	8,000	to	6,000
Neolithic	6,000	to	4,500
Civilization	4,500	to	*

*Oblivion, if Man is not careful.

Abbevillian Man was a savage Man in a primitive world. He walked erect, his features were coarse and animal-like, he was bearded and his body was hairy. His tools were rocks and clubs; only gradually he began to fashion weapons. Man generally went naked, crouched together in groups for warmth, and ate animal food raw. He lived in caves, or in the shelter of bushes and low trees. He probably had no family as such; mating, when it occurred, was apt to be at random and without knowledge that young would result.

Abbevillian Man

Acheulian Man was an improvement. He may have worn animal skins to protect his body and keep himself warm. His weapons were more carefully formed and more varied. He had learned to use and control fire, although anthropologists are not certain he could *make* fire. By this time, Man had begun to work and live with other men; a social order was beginning to emerge. Man probably began to fall naturally into family and social groups during this stage of human development. There was no compulsion to do this, except perhaps the basic need for common defense against mutual enemies. He was learning the relationship of cause and effect; he was learning to reason and think at an increasingly complex level.

Somewhere and sometime in the later Acheulian or early Mousterian stages, Man, the savage, learned how to cook the meat he hunted and ate. When he first controlled fire, it is a good guess that Man did not use the heat to cook food, but only to keep warm. Perhaps this primitive ancestor of ours stumbled over the burned carcass of a deer that had died in a forest fire, and being hungry, found the charred flesh good to the taste.

Mousterian (Neanderthal) Man took to natural caves for shelter. He conceived the idea of stone knives fastened to long poles, and thus was invented a primitive spear. He learned to tie things together with strips of animal hide and bones. He probably discovered the principles of the wheel, the lever, and the inclined plane, although there is no evidence to show that he used these devices.

Mousterian or Neanderthal Man

Acheulian Man

Mousterian Man was a little less "ugly" than his ancestors, and his general appearance was not so primitive or savage. He was still hairy, still bearded, probably unwashed and unkempt, too. But family groups had perhaps become fairly stable, and maybe even had some social meaning. Mousterian men cooperated with each other on an ever-increasing basis. That Man kept surviving, adapting, and spreading in a wild and hostile world, is clear evidence that he was thinking and reasoning more and more.

Lower Perigordian Man apparently was the first to turn weapons into tools. He began to invent tools to manufacture things he needed. He needed a particular kind of tool to make a particular kind of arrowhead; he

Lower Perigordian Man

required a needle to make many small skins into one large skin; he needed a round stone that fitted into a hollow stone, to grind nuts and acorns; he needed blades to shape wood and bones; he needed axes to cut firewood and shelter poles.

By comparison with modern Man, Lower Perigordian Man was a primitive Stone Age savage; by comparison with Abbevillian Man, he was a creative, ingenious, inventive creature who had progressed a considerable distance upward from savagery.

Aurignacian Man, 20 thousand years ago, was a prime example of the survival of the fittest. He was, at that time, the end product of about 580 thousand years of evolution and adaptation. We know this fellow more commonly as Cro-Magnon man, which is perhaps easier to say than Aurignacian Man. But just as his stage of physical development was temporary and transitional upon the Earth, it must be presumed that ours is, too.

Tools of the Lower Perigordian Man

Modern Man will continue to progress in thought and reason at an ever-increasing pace—unless, of course, he uses these precious faculties to obliterate his kind, and perhaps the Earth as well.

Man reached the Solutrean state of development at the end of the Stone Age; Magdalenian culture marks the beginning of modern Man. By constant improvement arising out of new ideas, Man's tools and weapons were now comparatively sophisticated. Clothing was nearly universal, food was varied as well as cooked, family groups were allied in larger groups, and Man could—as he wished —cooperate or fight with other men. Man's spiritual nature, as a part of his reason and thinking processes, found expression in primitive drawings on cave walls and in decorations and designs on clothing, weapons, and tools.

Man was ready, now, to bring to his native Planet Earth a condition we call civilization. He was ready now to build buildings, weave textiles, grow crops, domesticate animals, invent machines, and express ideas. He learned to do all of these things in the span of years we call the Mesolithic Age and Neolithic Age—from approximately 8,000 B.C. to 4,500 B.C. During these years, Man's civilization grew from the founding of the Biblical village of Jericho (about 7,500 B.C.) to the rise of the city of Sumer (about 2,000 B.C.).

With the dawn of civilization, Man began to gain dominion over his native Planet Earth.

Chapter VIII

THE EARTH IS A WORK OF ART

Nature has been called the Master Sculptor of Time, and with good reason. The whole Planet Earth is a massive work of art orbiting in space. The same probably applies to all the planets, in all the galaxies of space. But Man must, to some extent, merely speculate on what the other planets look like, whereas on his own planet Man can actually see what nature has wrought.

And the result is magnificent. The Earth yields Man natural resources for material uses, and much could be written of this aspect of the Earth. But Man has a curiosity arising from his spiritual nature, and the satisfaction he derives from his Planet Earth is not always on a material level.

Huge masses of mountains erupted and hardened

Nature's most useful tools have been weather and time. For a nearly-inconceivable span of years, nature has worked and toiled on a terrestrial masterpiece. From the viewpoint of eternity, the final sculpture is far from complete; indeed, it may well have only just begun. But from Man's viewpoint, the job may be nearing its end. If the awesome forces of nature Man is fooling around with should somehow be released from their ancient rhythms and patterns, the final touch of the sculptor's tools would be an obliterating blast. The terrestrial masterpiece would be smashed and Man as he is now would disappear forever.

Earlier it has been said that the Planet Earth was a sort of plastic sphere spinning on an axis and revolving in an orbit. As the Earth's outer crust hardened, the sculpting began. A similar process could be observed watching a plum dry into a prune. The Earth's surface wrinkled. The upthrust ridges became mountains, the downthrust ridges became valleys.

The Earth's crust cooled gradually, but probably not uniformly. The crust was thick and strong in some places, thin and weak in others. Roughly, the broad continental deserts and plains are the thick and strong parts of the Earth's crust.

Old Faithful at Yellowstone National Park

The weak and thin parts of the planet reacted to the powerful pressures within. Where the forces were too great to contain, the Earth's crust yielded and huge masses of mountains erupted and hardened. When the inner forces of the planet were very weak, the crust was sucked downward into abysses, chasms, crevasses, and holes. When the atmosphere developed and water began to appear, the low places filled with liquid and the high, cold places were covered with snow.

Man today can stand at the edge of North America's Grand Canyon and see a massive display of nature's handiwork on the Planet Earth. Here Man looks into yawning deeps. Exposed layers in the rocky canyon walls mutely tell what has happened there for millions upon millions of years.

Or Man can lift his eyes from the plains to the wind-swept frozen summit of Asia's Mt. Everest—awestruck before the thought of the power and might that thrust such a mountain (and its companions) upward into the sky.

The Earth's crust is thin in America's Yellowstone; some parts of the area are close to the Earth's inner fires, while other parts cut deeply into the Earth's cold crust. Within a few miles of each other lie the thousand-foot-deep Grand Canyon of the Yellowstone and the boiling mudpots, springs, and clear water hot springs and geysers of Norris Basin. Out in icy Yellowstone Lake, far from the shoreline, a very small upthrust pinnacle emits a steady stream of boiling water. The man who discovered

Caverns and caves lie just below the surface of the Earth

Yellowstone was John Coulter, and his descriptions of
the sights to be seen there caused the place to be known
for years as Coulter's Hell.

The Earth's crust is thick under the Russian steppes,
the African Sahara and veldt, the Argentine pampas, the
Australian desert and outback, the plains of North America. The planet's skin is richly carved in the fjords of
Norway, Sweden, New Zealand, and Zanzibar. The Earth
is veined with the surface channels of mighty rivers like
the Amazon, the Nile, the Mississippi, the Yangtze, the
Danube. Just beneath the surface of the Earth are com-
plexes of caves and caverns beyond counting.

Some of nature's handsomest carving on the Planet
Earth occurs in the American southwest. It is said that
no other continent can offer a sight to match the grandeur
and beauty of Bryce Canyon and Zion Canyon, of the

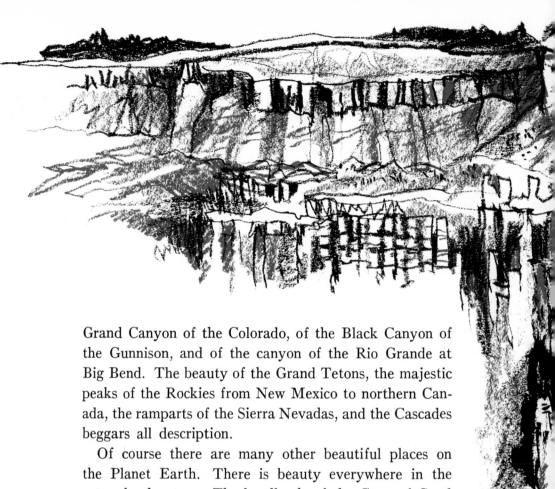

Grand Canyon of the Colorado, of the Black Canyon of the Gunnison, and of the canyon of the Rio Grande at Big Bend. The beauty of the Grand Tetons, the majestic peaks of the Rockies from New Mexico to northern Canada, the ramparts of the Sierra Nevadas, and the Cascades beggars all description.

Of course there are many other beautiful places on the Planet Earth. There is beauty everywhere in the artwork of nature. The headlands of the Cape of Good Hope, at the southern tip of Africa, are marvelous to see. So is the fantastic maze of islands that make up the wild and dangerous passage around Cape Horn at the southern tip of South America.

Perhaps the master sculptor could be accused of moods —nature was genial and arty in smoothing symmetrical mountains like Fujiyama, Paricutin, Popocatepetl, Rainier, Shasta, Hood; just the opposite with rough and vicious peaks like the Matterhorn, Everest, McKinley, and Moran.

Bryce Canyon, Utah

Nature may well have been confused when carving out the incredible channels of the monstrous Amazon. For 1,700 miles, this river flows through an impenetrable jungle called the Matto Grosso. The whole of the Amazon Basin, 1,465,637 squares miles of it, is flat and choked with jungle growth. Yet, beneath the verdant vegetation and the smooth, quiet waters, lies such a skein of channels as to stagger the human imagination.

The Earth is honeycombed with caves and caverns. Man knows many of them. Some of the best known are in the United States—Mammoth in Kentucky, Carlsbad in New Mexico, and Wind Cave in South Dakota. The natural caves all seem to be close to the Earth's surface. Some are the product of water erosion, others were created as accidents when erupting lava cooled abruptly or stony

Fujiyama, Japan

Rainbow Ridge, Utah

faults slid too far or not far enough in some ancient earthquake.

Natural bridges are a spectacular part of nature's sculpting on Earth. Best known to America is the soaring span of Rainbow Bridge in the badlands of Utah. This magnificent arch of stone is 275 feet from end to end, and the distance from its top to the canyon floor beneath is 309 feet. Once this beautiful piece of nature's handiwork in stone was a towering wall, a stony ridge upthrusting in the desert. Patiently, gently, nature cut away the softer parts. A million years or more have made it what the viewer sees today; in another million

Devils Tower

years or so, it may have been worn away entirely by the eternal sculpting of nature.

Still further evidence of nature's breathtaking skill are the colossal monoliths of Monument Valley. There on a flat plain stands a forest of soaring spires of stone, which the Indians called the Pillars of the Sky. Probably nothing so typifies the western part of the country to the average American as those giant stone monuments arising boldly from the smooth desert. Certainly few sights are more colorful than those fantastic red shafts.

One interesting piece of nature's art work is a Wyoming rampart known as Devil's Tower. This solitary butte was thrust from the Earth like a huge finger; it rises 1,280 feet above the prairie. Nothing else within miles is like it.

It would require volumes to describe the wonders that have been cut, coaxed, and shaped from the crust of the Earth by the master sculptor. What is set forth here, in word and picture, can only whet the curiosity for more.

Chapter IX

THE FUTURE OF MAN ON EARTH

There is reason to wonder what Man's future on Earth may be. Man has the technological skill and machinery to make Earth a paradise among planets. He also has the technological skill and machinery to make of the Earth a vast wasteland. To consider that such a catastrophic thing will happen is to give up hope that Man's better nature will eventually assert itself. Without hope, there is small reason to live.

So Man lives in the hope that some day all of his unique technological skill and machinery can be devoted to making Earth a paradise.

There is no doubt that within a few years machinery to create fresh water from salty sea water—economically

The Earth holds a wealth of natural resources

—will be available and in use. Such machinery actually exists today, but the cost is so prohibitive that conversion cannot be done on a large and sustained scale.

Man's need for new supplies of fresh water increase steadily, right along with the population. There are three billion people on Earth now; experts say that by the year 2,000, there will be six billion. Food cannot produce water, but water can produce food. Hence, an abundant supply of fresh water is the greatest concern for the future of Man on Earth. With plenty of water for the vast areas of now-barren dry country, food can eventually be produced to keep up with the growing world population.

Once Man harnesses all the capacities of the Earth's surface, he can turn his attention to the interior of the planet. There are surely resources within the Earth which Man has not tapped, and perhaps not even suspected. Some mention has been made earlier in this book of Man's efforts to know and understand his Earth. This examination and analysis of the Earth is proceeding faster and faster as scientists develop new instruments and tech-

niques. The Earth has a wealth of natural resources, unused and unknown, which will someday contribute materially to the future of Man on Earth.

Man's science and technology moves ahead swiftly on many fronts. Even while some men are exploring the Earth's surface and others are exploring the Earth's interior, still others are exploring the oceans and seas of the Earth. These great bodies of water are a part of the Earth. The deeps hold material treasures beyond imagination. Metals, minerals, and food can be taken from the oceans and seas of the Earth for generations to come. Man's future on Earth is only enhanced by the rich natural resources of the Earth's deep waters.

Few aspects of Man's relationship to his native Planet Earth are as spectacular to see and as stirring to the imagination as his plans to explore the vast reaches of space. Man has developed an incredible science; with it, this puny creature, only a little more than 600 thousand years old, dares to challenge the awesome mystery of time and space. Man's daring and audacity is such as to set his own mind and heart on fire with exultation.

Of all the creatures on Earth, Man alone has imagination. Perhaps it is this faculty that most sets Man apart from mere brutes. Imagination is *mental* creation, and once Man creates something in his mind, he is restless until he actually produces it.

The speed of Man's *mental* creative abilities greatly surpasses his *actual* creative abilities. Today, nearly every finished product that comes from an assembly line is obsolete before it can be marketed. Before a product can pass through the manufacturing process, another more adequate, more beautiful, more economical product has already been created on the artist's drawing boards. Sets of blueprints already exist for the superior product; and jigs, tools, dies, and fixtures are already in the works to

Huge icebergs may someday be melted for fresh water

produce the new and the better.

Thus, Man's imagination carries him ever forward at an accelerating speed. Yesterday's dreams are today's realities—and tomorrow's dreams will soon take their place in the galleries of Man's achievements.

Thus, Man, ever yielding to his insatiable nature, which yearns to achieve and create, is carried beyond the threshold of even his most optimistic dreams. Even as Man's rockets speed toward Venus to gather scientific information about the planets in space, Man plans new and bigger space probes of Mars and Saturn—and beyond into the endless reaches of space.

Perhaps some day, Man may leave his Planet Earth to pursue a new life on another planet.

Chapter X

OTHER EARTHS IN SPACE

And what of other Earths in the vastness of space? Among the billions of planets that orbit other suns in the galaxies of the universe, is Planet Earth the only one capable of sustaining life as Man knows it?

It can be assumed that the laws of physics, chemistry, and biology are generally the same throughout the universe. The same elements undoubtedly exist everywhere. If the same type of forces produce the same effects, there are at least 100,000,000,000,000,000,000 chances for planets similar to the Earth. There are at least that many suns in the known universe, and of course, each sun could nourish a planet similar to Earth.

121

But suppose only one sun in each thousand has a family of planets as does our sun. And of those suns that have planets, assume that only one in each thousand has a planet orbiting at the right distance for water and sunshine to encourage life forms. Of these, assume that only one in each thousand has a planet with mass and gravity enough to retain an atmosphere. Finally, assume that of the planets qualifying so far only one in each thousand has waters and atmosphere with the chemical composition to initiate and develop life. There would *still* be more than 100 million planets similar to Earth in the known universe.

Man's entire body of knowledge barely touches the staggering vastness of the universe. The largest and most complex electronic telescopes reach only a relatively short distance out into space. Is there a limit to the universe? Or is the universe without end? How can man visualize something that has no end? If a spaceship set forth from Earth and continued into the universe forever, how long and how far would it travel? Questions like these may never be answered. Perhaps the real miracle of the universe is not the universe itself, but men who can conceive of questions like these.

Planet Earth is about 4.5 billion years old. Some of the planets in space similar to Earth may be as much as 24 billion years old. Our Earth is an infant planet, in terms of time. Man appeared on Earth some time between 1.5 million and 600 thousand years ago. This is only a few moments measured by the gargantuan calendar

of eternity. Man on Earth has been "civilized" less than 6,000 years, but on some other planet men similar to Man may have been "civilized" for a thousand centuries. On some far distant Earth orbiting an even more distant sun, men and civilizations may have emerged a million years ago, or more. By comparison with beings on older planets in other galaxies of the universe, Earth Man may still be a mere savage.

Man on Planet Earth seems to have learned a great deal in the years since he emerged from the mists of time. But what he has learned is only a fragment of what remains to be learned. Soon, perhaps, Man will learn of other Earths and other Men.

INDEX

type specifications:

Text 12 on 15 Old Style No. 7
Major heads 18 Lydian Bold Italic
Captions 12 Garamond Italic